THIS BOOK BELONGS TO

....

PUSS IN BOOTS

Written by Helen Anderton
Illustrated by Stuart Lynch

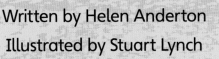

make
believe
ideas

Reading together

This book is designed to be fun for children who are gaining confidence in their reading. They will enjoy and benefit from some time discussing the story with an adult. Here are some ways you can help your child take those first steps in reading:

* Encourage your child to look at the pictures and talk about what is happening in the story.

* Help your child to find familiar words and sound out the letters in harder words.

* Ask your child to read and repeat each short sentence.

Look at rhymes

Many of the sentences in this book are simple rhymes. Encourage your child to recognise rhyming words. Try asking the following questions:

* What does this word say?

* Can you find a word that rhymes with it?

* Look at the ending of two words that rhyme. Are they spelt the same? For example, "plan" and "man", and "too" and "true".

Reading activities

The **What happens next?** activity encourages your child to retell the story and point to the mixed-up pictures in the right order.

The **Rhyming words** activity takes six words from the story and asks your child to read and find other words that rhyme with them.

The **Key words** pages provide practice with common words used in the context of the book. Read the sentences with your child and encourage him or her to make up more sentences using the key words listed around the border.

A **Picture dictionary** page asks children to focus closely on nine words from the story. Encourage your child to look carefully at each word, cover it with his or her hand, write it on a separate piece of paper, and finally, check it!

Do not complete all the activities at once – doing one each time you read will ensure that your child continues to enjoy the story and the time you are spending together. Have fun!

A mean old miller died one day,
and written in his will,
he gave two sons the house and horse,
while the cat was left to Bill.

Bill asked his brothers, "Can't you help?"
    (He was in a tricky spot.)
But they said, "Go! And take that cat,"
    leaving Bill with not a lot.

Bill said, "Oh, what can I do?
Perhaps I'll eat my cat!"
But the crafty cat, on hearing this,
said, "Hey! Please don't do that!"

Said Puss, "Buy me a bag and boots –
    I'll make your dreams come true.
Trust me, and I will bring you gold,
    a wife and a palace too."

Thrilled, Bill found a bag and boots.
Then Puss said, "Here's the plan:
we'll take some gifts to please the king –
and make you a wealthy man."

Puss caught a rabbit in the bag,
and then he made a stew.
"I'll take this to the king," he said,
"and say it comes from you."

Puss gave many gifts this way –
    delivering them by hand.
He told the king, "They're from Lord Stone!"
    (To make young Bill sound grand.)

"Now," Puss said, "trust me once more.
Go take a morning swim."
And while Bill swam, Puss stole his clothes –
which put Bill in a spin!

Just then the royal coach came past,
    so Puss said with a grin,
"Sire, Lord Stone's been robbed by thieves!"
    Said the king to Bill, "Come in!"

The princess gave Bill smart new clothes,
    and to thank her for this kindness,
Puss said, "Sire, at Lord Stone's home
    we've a feast for you and Her Highness!"

Puss had one thing left to do.
He ran ahead to find
a palace lived in by a troll –
the mean and nasty kind.

ROAR!

This troll could change into a bee,
a lion or a seal.
Puss thought, "If I can trick the troll,
his palace is mine to steal."

Said Puss, "Now, Troll, I hear it's true
you can be a lion or bee.
I picture you as a fierce beast,
but it's a MOUSE I'd like to see."

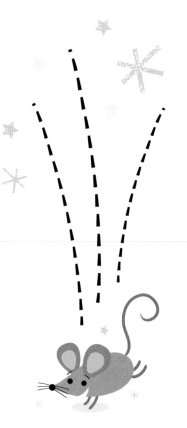

With that, the troll became a mouse –
right there on the floor!
In a flash, Puss ate him up
and wrote "Lord Stone" on the door.

Lord
Stone

Lord
Stone

Puss stood proudly at the door
as the royal coach arrived.
The king was amazed and said to Bill:
"Take my daughter as your bride!"

23

Bill had all that he could want
with a palace and his wife.
And Puss in Boots was free to live
a long and happy life!

24

What happens next?

Some of the pictures from the story have been mixed up! Can you retell the story and point to each picture in the correct order?

Rhyming words

Read the words in the middle of each group and point to the other words that rhyme with them.

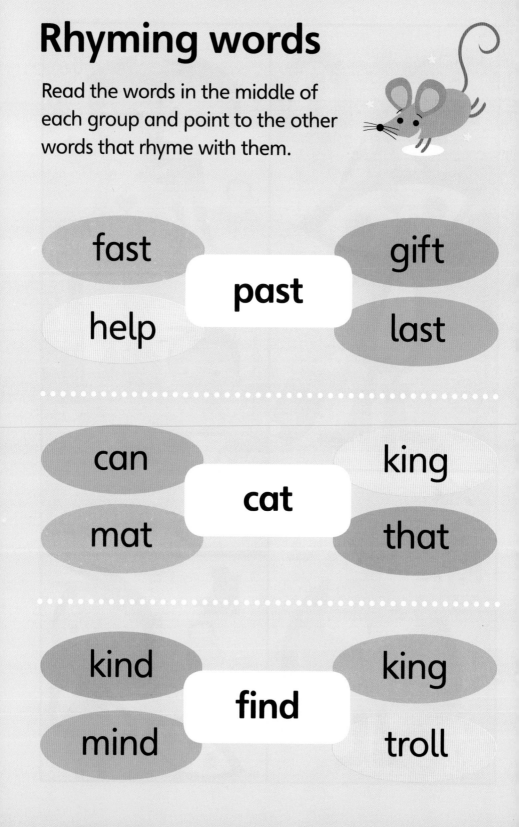

fast

gift

past

help

last

can

king

cat

mat

that

kind

king

find

mind

troll

puss

rabbit

seal

real

steal

door

see

bee

stew

tea

knife

life

wife

lion

boots

Now choose a word and make up a rhyming chant!

I **see** a **bee** drinking **tea!**

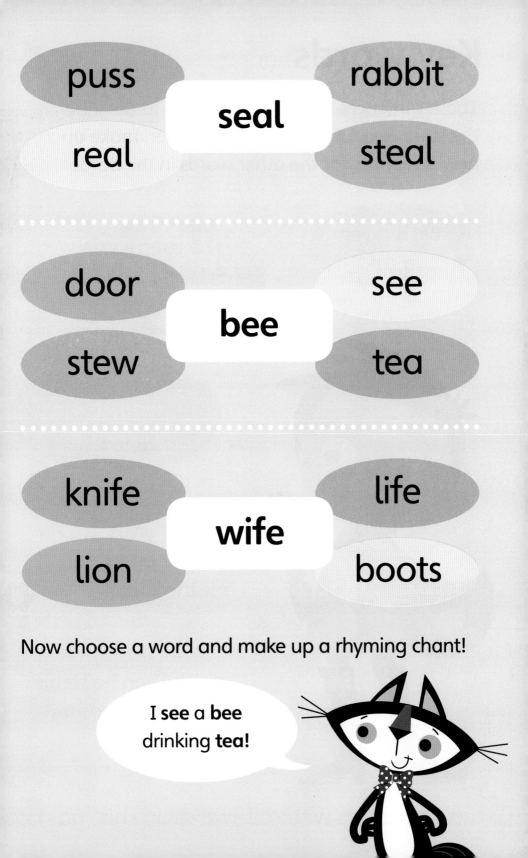

Key words

These sentences use common words to describe the story. Read the sentences and then make up new sentences for the other words in the border.

Bill **is** given a cat.

The cat asks Bill **for** a bag and boots.

Puss in Boots says he will **help** Bill.

Puss gives a rabbit **to** the king.

Then he steals Bill's clothes!

like · very

· are · but · saw · with · all · we · help · his · go · not

Picture dictionary

Look carefully at the pictures and the words.
Now cover the words, one at a time.
Can you remember how to write them?

bag

boots

coach

gold

palace

rabbit

stew

troll

wife

Comparing Past and Present

Going to School

Rebecca Rissman

Raintree is an imprint of Capstone Global Library Limited, a company incorporated in England and Wales having its registered office at 7 Pilgrim Street, London, EC4V 6LB – Registered company number: 6695582

www.raintreepublishers.co.uk
myorders@raintreepublishers.co.uk

Text © Capstone Global Library Limited 2014
First published in hardback in 2014
Paperback edition first published in 2015
The moral rights of the proprietor have been asserted.

Edited by Rebecca Rissman, Daniel Nunn, and Catherine Veitch
Designed by Philippa Jenkins
Picture research by Elizabeth Alexander
Production by Helen McCreath
Originated by Capstone Global Library Ltd
Printed and bound in China

ISBN 978 1 4062 7147 8 (hardback)
17 16 15 14 13
10 9 8 7 6 5 4 3 2 1

ISBN 978 1 4062 7154 6 (paperback)
18 17 16 15 14
10 9 8 7 6 5 4 3 2 1

British Library Cataloguing in Publication Data
A full catalogue record for this book is available from the British Library.

Acknowledgements
We would like to thank the following for permission to reproduce photographs: Alamy pp. 7 (© redsnapper), 10 (© ClassicStock); Corbis p. 9 (© Yi Lu/Viewstock); Getty Images pp. 6 (Keystone-France/Gamma-Keystone), 11 (Siri Stafford/Lifesize), 12 (Brooke/Topical Press Agency/Hulton Archive), 13 (Christopher Futcher/the Agency Collection), 14 (Kurt Hutton/Picture Post), 18 (Kurt Hutton/Picture Post), 23 (Kurt Hutton/Picture Post); 20 (Mary Evans Picture Library); Shutterstock pp. 5 (© Monkey Business Images), 15 (© AVAVA), 17 (© Pressmaster), 19 (© Zurijeta), 21 (© Monkey Business Images), 23 (© AVAVA); Superstock pp. 4 (Underwood Photo Archives), 8 (Underwood Photo Archives), 16 (ClassicStock.com), 22 (ClassicStock.com).

Front cover photographs of pupils and teachers of the Steamer Class in the Washington School, Massachusetts reproduced with permission of Library of Congress (Lewis Wickes Hine), and a primary school pupil doing an assignment reproduced with permission of Getty Images (PhotoAlto/Odilon Dimier). Back cover photograph of primary school pupils reading books in front of a blackboard, 1930s, reproduced with permission of Superstock (ClassicStock.com).

We would like to thank Nancy Harris and Diana Bentley for their invaluable help in the preparation of this book.

Every effort has been made to contact copyright holders of material reproduced in this book. Any omissions will be rectified in subsequent printings if notice is given to the publisher.

Contents

Comparing the past and present

Things in the past have already happened.

Things in the present are happening now.

Schools have changed over time.

Schools in the present are very different to schools in the past.

Schools

In the past most schools were small. Some had only one room!

Today, many schools are very large.

Getting to school

In the past many children walked a long way to school.

Today, many children ride
in cars or buses to school.

Classes

In the past children of all ages were in the same class.

Today, most schools place children into different classes by their ages.

School supplies

In the past many children wrote on small blackboards.

Today, children write on paper or type on computers.

In the past schools had few books for children to read.

Today, school libraries have
many books for children to read.

In the past children learned things by asking teachers and reading books.

Today, children can use a computer to learn things. They can also ask teachers and read books.

19

Lucky pupils

In the past only some lucky children could go to school.

Today, many children can go
to school.

Then and now

In the past children enjoyed going to school. Today, children still enjoy school!

Picture glossary

 **blackboard** dark writing surface. People write with chalk on blackboards.

 **computer** machine that helps people write and learn

Index

Notes for parents and teachers

Before reading

Talk to children about the differences between the past and present. Explain that things that have already happened are in the past. Ask children to describe their activities from the previous day. Tell children that all of those activities happened in the past. Then explain that the conversation you are having now is happening in the present.

After reading

- Explain to children that the experience of going to school has changed in many ways over time. Ask children to describe their classroom, emphasizing the school materials, class size, and technology. Then ask children to brainstorm about how their experience is different from what children might have experienced in the past.

- Ask children to turn to pages 14–15. Show children the two images, contrasting the technology in modern classrooms with what children used in the past. Then ask children if they can think of any other technology they use at school that did not exist in the past. Keep a record of their ideas on the board, and add any that they might have missed. Remember to include electricity, telephones, and running water.